If you scare a flamingo

Written by Keith Faulkner
Illustrated by Jonathan Lambert

Flying Frog Publishing

If someone gave you a big sloppy kiss,
How do you think you'd react to this?

Blush?

If you went to a land of ice and snow,
How would you feel there—do you know?

Cold?

If you're out in the desert in the midday sun,
How would you feel—would this be fun?

Hot?

If you were in a boat on a rough, rough sea,
How would you feel, can you please tell me?